The Joy of Christmas

CELEBRATE THE SEASON

CREATED BY
PHIL BARFOOT

ARRANGED AND ORCHESTRATED BY
DAVE WILLIAMSON

PRODUCTS AVAILABLE

Choral Book 1-4158-5578-1
Listening CD* 1-4158-5582-X
Accompaniment CD (split track) 1-4158-5583-8
Rehearsal Tracks 1-4158-5593-5
Orchestration 1-4158-5596-X
CD Promo Pak 1-4158-5602-8

* Listening CDs are available at a reduced rate when purchased in quantities of 10 or more.

WORSHIP MUSIC GROUP

1-4158-5578-1

FOREWORD

JOY

FAMILY

CELEBRATION

LOVE HOPE PEACE

LAUGHTER WONDER WARMTH

JESUS

There are countless words that describe the spectrum of emotions, elements, feelings and traditions that all of us look forward to year after year as we celebrate this very special and unique season.

Like the "word tree" above, for our celebration to be complete, all these qualities must be firmly rooted and founded upon the One whose birthday we celebrate: JESUS.

The passion and purpose that has driven us in creating *"The Joy of Christmas"* is to offer *songs* that create *moments* that include *all* the elements you'll need for an effective Christmas production: i.e., an upbeat opener, a carol sing-along, a shepherds' moment, a kings' processional, a candlelighting moment, children's choir involvement, a big band secular carol medley, a "contemporary classical" medley, a fun "Twelve Days of Christmas" moment, a song to set the tone for the invitation, etc. It is our desire that these "moments" will facilitate your efforts in leading your congregation and community in worship this Christmas season.

I would like to personally thank you for your overwhelming response to the first five choral collections in this series: *Portraits of Christmas, Colors of Christmas, Treasures of Christmas, The Spirit of Christmas* and *The Glory of Christmas.*

I am honored to be offering this project to you through LifeWay Worship Music Group. Their awesome team, under the direction of Mike Harland, has been incredibly supportive and possesses a sincere desire to help the local church Music Ministry by providing ministry products and tools that result in genuine worship.

I am also very excited to partner once again with my good friend (and incredibly talented arranger), Dave Williamson. You'll *love* his fresh and inspired orchestrations!

I encourage you to explore a *variety* of effective uses for this collection (see "suggested uses" on the following page).

God's BEST to you as you experience *"The Joy of Christmas"* this season.

Blessings!

Phil Barfoot

SUGGESTED USES

Whether your Christmas needs include utilizing an entire collection or compiling music for a Pageant, Living Christmas Tree, Christmas Dessert, Christmas Concert or music for those "December Sundays," it is our desire that *"The Joy of Christmas"* will provide a refreshing resource for your Music Ministry this Christmas season!

John Plastow has created an optional narration and drama script with special production notes and ideas that will enhance the ministry and effectiveness of your presentation. These helpful tools can provide creative continuity to your concert.

You can find this online at *www.lifeway.com/worshipmusic*.

Also, if you would like to record this project with your choir and soloists, CHRISTIAN COPYRIGHT ALLIANCE can handle *all* the details for you. We have recorded over 450 choirs and would love to work with you. You can "mix and match" any of the songs in this collection with our large library of trax from the finest arrangers in choral music. For more information, contact Phil Barfoot or Gelsie Hahn at:

Christian Copyright Alliance
3326 Aspen Grove Drive
Suite 140
Franklin, TN 37067
615-771-2665/ 615-771-2632 fax
ccapbarfoot@comcast.net

CONTENTS

John Plastow has created an optional narration and drama script with special production notes and ideas that will enhance the ministry and effectiveness of your presentation. These helpful tools can provide creative continuity to your concert. You can find this online at *www.lifeway.com/worshipmusic*.

The Season of Joy
with Joy to the World!
(optional opener)

Words and Music by
PHIL BARFOOT
and REBECCA J. PECK
Arranged by Dave Williamson

CHOIR: unison

The sea - son of joy, the sea - son of

JOY TO THE WORLD! (Isaac Watts/George Frederick Handel)

Open your heart

and you will dis - cov - er

good - will and good cheer. It's the

best time of _____ the year! _____

The sea - son of joy, _____

_____ sea - son of joy, _____ sea - son of

unison

unison

Joy! A Carol Medley
for Choir and Congregation
includes How Great Our Joy,
Angels We Have Heard on High, The First Noel
and Thou Didst Leave Thy Throne

Arranged by Dave Williamson

Joy, joy, joy, joy!

CHOIR and Optional CONGREGATION
unison

1. While by our sheep we watched at night,

(Drums cont. march through rests)

Glad tid-ings brought an an-gel bright. How great our joy!

ANGELS WE HAVE HEARD ON HIGH (Traditional French Carol)

1. An - gels we have
2. Come to Beth - le -

heard on high, Sweet - ly sing - ing o'er the plains:
hem, and see Him whose birth the an - gels sing;

THE FIRST NOEL (English Carol, 17th century)

THOU DIDST LEAVE THY THRONE (Emily E. S. Elliott/Timothy R. Matthews)

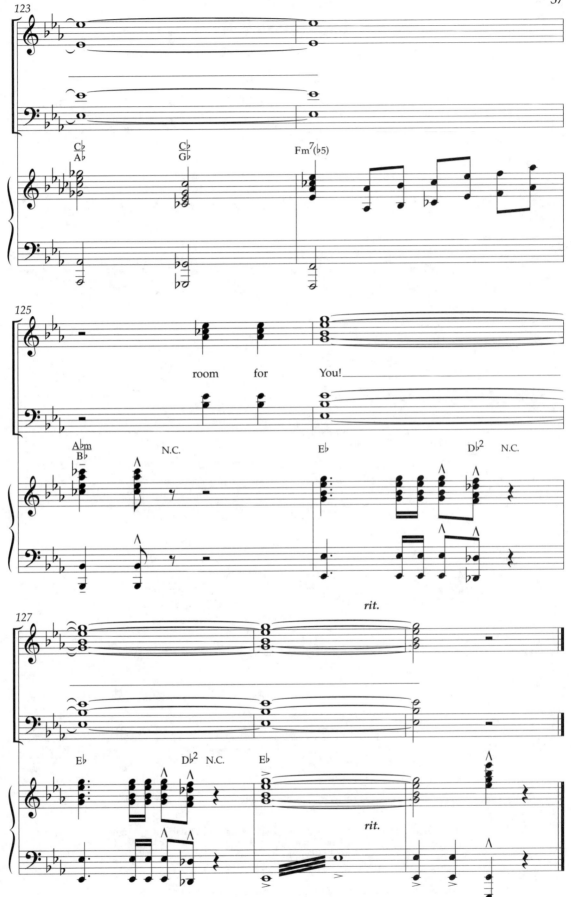

Follow On
with I Have Decided to Follow Jesus
(optional King's Processional)

Words and Music by
PHIL BARFOOT
and REBECCA J. PECK
Arranged by Dave Williamson

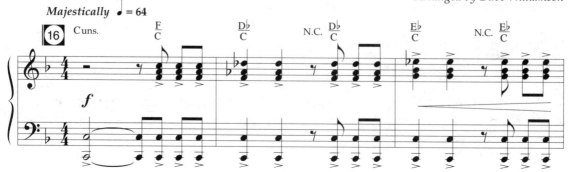

NOTE: If using a solo instead of trio, soloist should sing solo 1, 2 and 3 and sing regular size notes through trio sections (melody).

seek - ing the Mes - si - ah, ho - ly prom - ised One.

SOLO 2
mp

See - ing His star, a sure and guid - ing light,

17

MEN'S TRIO: *unison*
mf

lead - ing to the birth - place of God's Son. We will

fol - low___ on!

2. Hold - ing to___ the truth,

SOLO 3 *mf*

trust - ing in___ His plan,   long - ing just to bow___ in wor - ship

ALL 3

at___ His_ feet, know-ing ver - y soon we'll see the great_ I AM.

Csus   C   F²(no3)   E♭⁶₉

D. S. al Coda
(to meas. 15)

Crown Him Lord of lords_ and King of kings! We will

D♭maj⁷   Csus   C   Csus C

D. S. al Coda
(to meas. 15)

⊕ CODA   *Choir*   I HAVE DECIDED TO FOLLOW JESUS *(Author Unknown/Folk Melody from India)*

fol - low___ on! We have de - cid - ed to fol-low

⊕ CODA   *f unison*

fol - low___ on! We have de - cid - ed to fol-low

unison

⊕ CODA   B♭   C   F   F   F/E♭   D♭   D♭sus/E♭

f

A Classical Christmas

includes Hallelujah, Amen!,
Jesu, Joy of Man's Desiring
and For Unto Us a Child Is Born

Arranged by Dave Williamson

HALLELUJAH, AMEN! *(from "Judas Maccabaeus" by Handel /Morell)*

Hal - le - lu - jah, A-men, A-men, Hal - le - lu - jah, A - men.

52

JESU, JOY OF MAN'S DESIRING
(New lyrics by Phil Barfoot and Rebecca J. Peck/Music by J.S. Bach)

si - lent, ho - ly__ Christ - mas night.

Hal - le - lu - jahs we will_ glad - ly raise!

Great Joy

Words and Music by
PHIL BARFOOT
and REBECCA J. PECK
Arranged by Dave Williamson

27

sud-den-ly__ ap-pear-ing;__ the shep-herds stood__ and trem-

bled at__ the sight.__ But__ the

(SOLO)

an - gel said,_ "Fear not!__ Go to Beth - le - hem.__

CHOIR
mf

Ooo,__ Ooo,__

it from_ the_ hills,_ sing it in_ the streets._

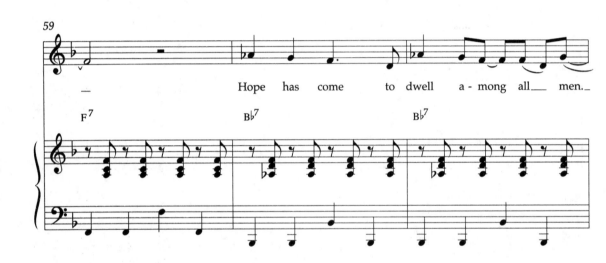

Hope has come to dwell a-mong all_ men._

God_ in hu-man form,_

lit - tle ba - by Boy. Great joy,

great joy!

Great, great joy,

Underneath the Tree
with Near the Cross

Words and Music by
PHIL BARFOOT
and REBECCA J. PECK
Arranged by Dave Williamson

1. As a child on Christ-mas morn-ing, I would kneel be-fore the tree and my eyes would dance with won-der when I

A Big Band Christmas

includes We Wish You the Merriest,
Have a Holly, Jolly Christmas *and*
It's the Most Wonderful Time of the Year

Arranged by Dave Williamson

WE WISH YOU THE MERRIEST (Les Brown)

HAVE A HOLLY, JOLLY CHRISTMAS (Johnny Marks)

Christ - mas this year!

IT'S THE MOST WONDERFUL TIME OF THE YEAR (Eddie Pola and George Wyle)

It's the most won-der-ful time_____ of the year with the kids jin-gle-bell-ing and

It's the most won - der - ful time

of the year!

Big band swing! ♩ = 146

unison Listesso

Listesso, with a swing!

Go Tell Everyone

Words and Music by
DAN SCOTT,
TANYA GOODMAN SYKES,
and MICHAEL SYKES
Arranged by Dave Williamson

1. Long lay the world 'neath the

2. Just as _____ the proph-ets had prom - ised be - fore, _____

Ooo, _____

He came _ pro-claim-ing the year _____ of _____ the Lord.

Ooo, _____

vic-to-ry's_ been won._____ Go_____ and

Bb

Bbm/G Bbm/A Bbm F/C

51 (1st time) 2nd time to Coda ⊕
54 (2nd time) (to meas. 48)

tell ev - er - y - one.

F/C C⁷ 2nd time to Coda ⊕
(to meas. 48) F

mf (SOLO back in, with continued freedom)

3. We've been____ com-mis-sioned_ to car - ry the flame,_ and

Bb/C F G⁷ C⁷

mf

123

calling us to go._____ Ho,_____

calling us to go, to go, to go.

SOLO ad lib. with CHOIR to end

Go,_____ tell_____ ev - er - y -

56

Go, tell ev - er - y -

one. E - vil is____ de - feat - ed and the

vic - to - ry's____ been won.____

Mary Had a Baby
with Glory Hallelujah to the Newborn King

Additional lyrics by
PHIL BARFOOT

St. HELENA ISLAND SPIRITUAL
Arranged by Dave Williamson

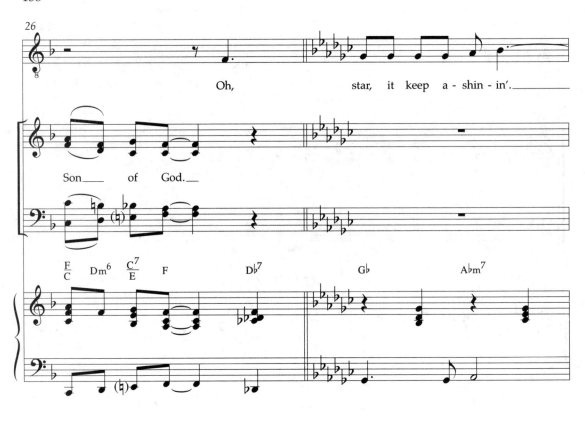

140

GLORY HALLELUJAH TO THE NEWBORN KING
(Traditional Spiritual)

143

Light of Hope
with Silent Night
(optional candlelighting moment)

Words and Music by
PHIL BARFOOT
and REBECCA J. PECK
Arranged by Dave Williamson

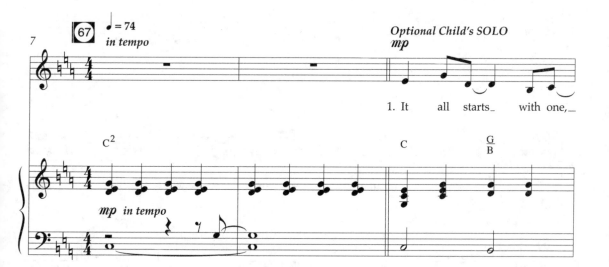

one can - dle in___ the dark - ness. I

add ADULT (with CHILD)
(*mp*)

reach my hand___ to yours;___ to - geth - er we make___ a dif -

f'rence, and the dark - ness soon___ is gone___ as the

1st time: WOMEN (Parts) , with Opt. CHILDREN'S CHOIR singing melody; MEN tacet
2nd time: ALL (Parts) , with Opt. CHILDREN'S CHOIR singing melody to end

for that's when love____ shines bright._____

D.S. al Coda
(to meas. 21)

CODA

light of hope.

A little slower ♩ = 70

CHOIR with opt. CHILDREN'S CHOIR on melody

f Stronger

Lift up your can - dle, and I'll____ lift up mine.____

SILENT NIGHT *(Joseph Mohr/Franz Grüber)*
WOMEN *with opt.* CHILDREN'S CHOIR

Si - lent night, ho - ly

night, All is calm,

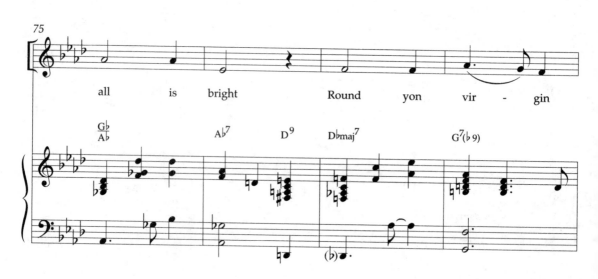

all is bright Round yon vir - gin

The Twelve Days of Christmas

TRADITIONAL ENGLISH
Arranged by David Williamson

NOTE: For creative production ideas, go to www.lifeway.com/worshipmusic.

CHOIR MEMBER: (shouted loudly) "This is gonna be just beautiful!"

169

Slower ♩ = 116

135

eight maids a-milk-ing,

D7   D7/F♯   D7/A   N.C.

Slower

(a few men from the choir "moo" randomly—"cow sounds")

138

sev-en swans a-swim-ming,

D7   D7/F♯   D7/A   N.C.

82

141

six geese a-lay-ing,

D7   D7/F♯   D7/A

Gm   E♭   Gm

"Classical" feel